Visit us at www.kidsbooks.com

FIND
FREDDIE & LISA

IN THE

HAUNTED HOUSE

Freddie and Lisa have discovered a house that is unlike any other—a haunted house!

FIND FREDDIE & LISA AT THE HAUNTED HOUSE, AND THESE FUN ITEMS:

- ☐ Apples (2)
- ☐ Baseball cap
- ☐ Bones (3)
- ☐ Box
- ☐ Burned-out candle
- ☐ Clothespin
- ☐ Coffeepot
- ☐ Crown
- ☐ Dog
- ☐ Duck
- ☐ Eyeglasses
- ☐ Faucet
- ☐ Fish tank
- ☐ Ghosts (3)
- ☐ Hammer
- ☐ Heart
- ☐ Kite
- ☐ Lips
- ☐ Mouse
- ☐ Owl
- ☐ Paint bucket
- ☐ Peanut
- ☐ Pencils (2)
- ☐ Piggy bank
- ☐ Saw
- ☐ Sock
- ☐ Submarine
- ☐ Truck
- ☐ Umbrella

Should they go in?
Should they stay in?
What do you think they should do?

FIND FREDDIE & LISA BEFORE THEY DECIDE, AND THESE FUN ITEMS:

- ❑ Birds (2)
- ❑ Blimps (2)
- ❑ Bowling ball
- ❑ Broom
- ❑ Camel
- ❑ Candle
- ❑ Chef's hat
- ❑ Feather
- ❑ Flower
- ❑ Football
- ❑ Giraffe
- ❑ Jester
- ❑ King
- ❑ Laundry
- ❑ Lost boot
- ❑ Mustache
- ❑ Napoleon
- ❑ Painted egg
- ❑ Rabbit
- ❑ Red wagon
- ❑ Sailboat
- ❑ Short pants
- ❑ Skull
- ❑ Sled
- ❑ Slide
- ❑ Star
- ❑ Top hats (2)
- ❑ Trash can
- ❑ Umbrella

Ready, set, go! Everyone runs toward the door of the haunted house, but only two enter it!

FIND FREDDIE & LISA AS THEY MEET THE MONSTERS, AND THESE FUN ITEMS:

- ❑ Apple
- ❑ Arrow
- ❑ Bag
- ❑ Balloon
- ❑ Banana peel
- ❑ Baseball cap
- ❑ Bone
- ❑ Boot
- ❑ Broken heart
- ❑ Broom
- ❑ Cake
- ❑ Candles (5)
- ❑ Crystal ball
- ❑ Fish
- ❑ Genie
- ❑ Ghosts (2)
- ❑ Ice-cream cone
- ❑ Lightning
- ❑ Necktie
- ❑ Owl
- ❑ Piano
- ❑ Skulls (5)
- ❑ Snake
- ❑ Spoon
- ❑ Tombstone

Ms. Witch makes gross snacks. Her specialty is the "Everything Goes" sandwich!

FIND FREDDIE & LISA AT SNACK TIME, AND THESE FUN ITEMS:

- ☐ Accordion
- ☐ Apple
- ☐ Baseball
- ☐ Blackbird
- ☐ Bone
- ☐ Candle
- ☐ Checkerboard
- ☐ Drill
- ☐ Earring
- ☐ Fish (2)
- ☐ Flower
- ☐ Fork
- ☐ Frying pan
- ☐ Grapes
- ☐ Green cup
- ☐ Heart
- ☐ Helmet
- ☐ Ice-cream cone
- ☐ Ladle
- ☐ Neckties (2)
- ☐ Oilcan
- ☐ Orange
- ☐ Palm tree
- ☐ Pear
- ☐ Rolling pin
- ☐ Saw
- ☐ Sock
- ☐ Stool
- ☐ Toaster
- ☐ Wooden spoon

Freddie and Lisa begin to explore the haunted house. A wrong turn, and down they tumble!

FIND FREDDIE & LISA IN THE DUNGEON, AND THESE FUN ITEMS:

- ❑ Airplane
- ❑ Balloon
- ❑ Banana peel
- ❑ Bowling ball
- ❑ Broken egg
- ❑ Broom
- ❑ Candy cane
- ❑ Corn
- ❑ Cupcake
- ❑ Doctor
- ❑ Drum
- ❑ Fire hydrant
- ❑ Flowerpot
- ❑ Flying bat
- ❑ Football
- ❑ Hot dog
- ❑ Ice-cream cone
- ❑ Ice-cream pop
- ❑ Mummies (3)
- ❑ Piggy bank
- ❑ Rabbit
- ❑ Roller skates
- ❑ Scarecrow
- ❑ Shark
- ❑ Skateboard
- ❑ Skulls (2)
- ❑ Skunk
- ❑ Top hat
- ❑ Umbrellas (2)
- ❑ Wagon

Next to the dungeon are the wildest lanes in town. It's a great place to do anything—but bowl!

FIND FREDDIE & LISA AT THE GHOSTLY BOWLING ALLEY, AND THESE FUN ITEMS:

- ☐ Arrow
- ☐ Balloon
- ☐ Bird
- ☐ Boot
- ☐ Broken ball
- ☐ Broom
- ☐ Cactus
- ☐ Candles (2)
- ☐ Carrot
- ☐ Dog
- ☐ Earphones
- ☐ Flower
- ☐ Hamburger
- ☐ Hot dog
- ☐ Mouse
- ☐ Mummy
- ☐ Mummy's ball
- ☐ Orange
- ☐ Pear
- ☐ Periscope
- ☐ Robot
- ☐ Sailboat
- ☐ Snowman
- ☐ Spring
- ☐ Sunglasses (2 pairs)
- ☐ Sword
- ☐ Tennis racket
- ☐ Tombstone
- ☐ Yo-yo

Dr. Frankenstein has lots of patients who need lots of patience.

FIND FREDDIE & LISA IN DR. FRANKENSTEIN'S LABORATORY, AND THESE FUN ITEMS:

- ❑ Black cat
- ❑ Book
- ❑ Bride
- ❑ Bunny
- ❑ Candle
- ❑ Cheese
- ❑ Dog
- ❑ Dracula
- ❑ Duck
- ❑ Feather
- ❑ Greeting card
- ❑ Ice-cream pop
- ❑ Invisible person
- ❑ Paintbrush
- ❑ Paint bucket
- ❑ Pickax
- ❑ Roller skates
- ❑ Sailor
- ❑ Saw
- ❑ Screwdriver
- ❑ Shovel
- ❑ Skull
- ❑ Suspenders
- ❑ Television
- ❑ Three-legged thing
- ❑ Tulip
- ❑ Two-headed thing
- ❑ Watch
- ❑ Wooden block

The monsters walk very carefully when they visit *this* room!

FIND FREDDIE & LISA IN THE COBWEB ROOM, AND THESE FUN ITEMS:

- ☐ Baby carriage
- ☐ Binoculars
- ☐ Bow tie
- ☐ Boxing glove
- ☐ Broom
- ☐ Cup
- ☐ Dog
- ☐ Duck
- ☐ Earring
- ☐ Electric plug
- ☐ Fish
- ☐ Flower
- ☐ Football helmet
- ☐ Fork
- ☐ Ghosts (2)
- ☐ Hammer
- ☐ Heart
- ☐ Key
- ☐ Lock
- ☐ Mummy
- ☐ Old-fashioned radio
- ☐ Pencil
- ☐ Quarter moon
- ☐ Ring
- ☐ Robot
- ☐ Screwdriver
- ☐ Ship
- ☐ Skull
- ☐ Top hat
- ☐ Turtles (2)
- ☐ Wagon

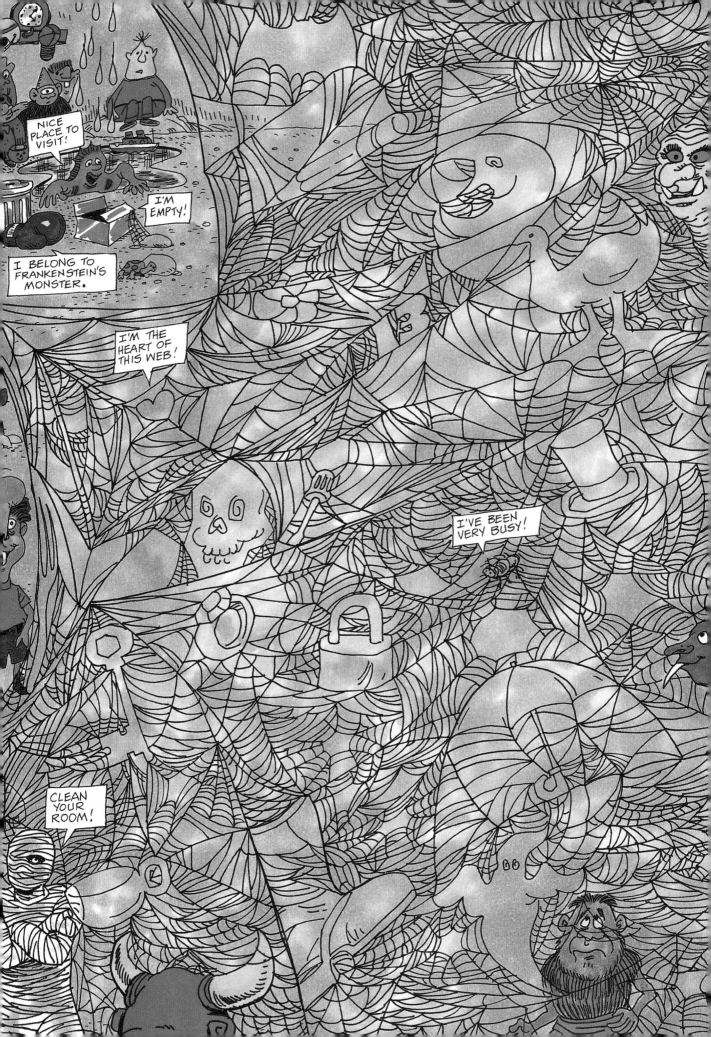

Playtime for monsters!

FIND FREDDIE & LISA IN THE MONSTERS' PLAYROOM, AND THESE FUN ITEMS:

- ☑ Artist
- ☑ Balloon
- ❑ Banana peel
- ❑ Barbell
- ❑ Birds (2)
- ❑ Blackboard
- ❑ Crayons (5)
- ❑ Donkey
- ❑ Fish
- ❑ Football
- ❑ Haunted house
- ❑ Hole in the baseball bat
- ❑ Hood
- ❑ Ice skate
- ❑ Jack-o'-lanterns (4)
- ❑ Jacks (4)
- ❑ Joke book
- ❑ Juggler
- ❑ Mask
- ❑ Monster puppet
- ❑ Mummy doll
- ❑ Musician
- ❑ Nail
- ❑ Pail
- ❑ Pogo stick
- ❑ Rubber ducky
- ❑ Sailboat
- ❑ Snake
- ❑ Telephone
- ❑ Tricycle
- ❑ Turtle
- ❑ Wind-up monster

It is time for Freddie and Lisa to go. The friendly monsters hope their new friends will return soon.

FIND FREDDIE & LISA LEAVING THE HAUNTED HOUSE, AND THESE FUN ITEMS:

- ❑ Apple
- ❑ Arrow
- ❑ Balloon
- ❑ Birds (2)
- ❑ Box
- ❑ Broken heart
- ❑ Brooms (2)
- ❑ Candles (2)
- ❑ Clock
- ❑ Crown
- ❑ Dog
- ❑ Duck
- ❑ Envelope
- ❑ Flower
- ❑ Ice skates
- ❑ Key
- ❑ Ladder
- ❑ Lamp
- ❑ Mouse
- ❑ Painted egg
- ❑ Periscope
- ❑ Quarter moon
- ❑ Rabbit
- ❑ Roller skates
- ❑ Shovel
- ❑ Skull
- ❑ TV camera
- ❑ Umbrella

Freddie and Lisa are here
with a few of their playmates:

Bunny Honey   Sam
Donald   Santa
Frankie   Santa's helpers: Fee, Fi, Fo, and Fun
Hector   Susie
Laura

MONSTER MADNESS

There once was an old house, in an old part of town, that was discovered by two children. They wanted to go inside, but first they had to find the following hidden pictures. Can you help them?

- ❑ Banana
- ❑ Bone
- ❑ Book
- ❑ Boot
- ❑ Bottle
- ❑ Broom
- ❑ Carrot
- ❑ Elephant
- ❑ Envelope
- ❑ Fish
- ❑ Flower
- ❑ Hairbrush
- ❑ Hammer
- ❑ Heart
- ❑ Hockey stick
- ❑ Horseshoe
- ❑ Hot dog
- ❑ Lost wallet
- ❑ Owl
- ❑ Palm tree
- ❑ Rabbit
- ❑ Sailboat
- ❑ Saw
- ❑ Screwdriver
- ❑ Skull
- ❑ Snake
- ❑ Star
- ❑ Toothbrush
- ❑ Zipper

In the old house was an old trunk, which the children opened with an old key. Out of the trunk came many strange things, including these hidden objects:

- ❑ Arrow
- ❑ Balloon
- ❑ Bearded man
- ❑ Carrot
- ❑ Chicken
- ☒ Fish
- ☒ Giraffe
- ❑ Horse
- ❑ Kite
- ☒ Mouse
- ❑ Quarter moon
- ☒ Snowman
- ❑ Tepee
- ☒ Tombstone
- ❑ Turtle
- ☒ Unicorn

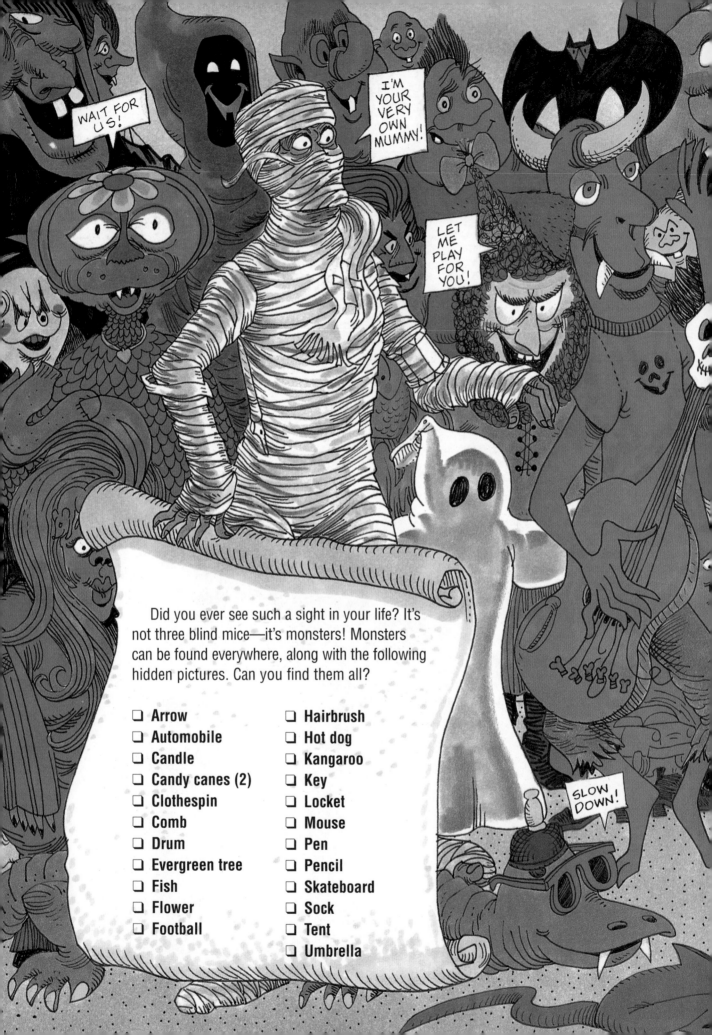

Did you ever see such a sight in your life? It's not three blind mice—it's monsters! Monsters can be found everywhere, along with the following hidden pictures. Can you find them all?

- ❑ Arrow
- ❑ Automobile
- ❑ Candle
- ❑ Candy canes (2)
- ❑ Clothespin
- ❑ Comb
- ❑ Drum
- ❑ Evergreen tree
- ❑ Fish
- ❑ Flower
- ❑ Football
- ❑ Hairbrush
- ❑ Hot dog
- ❑ Kangaroo
- ❑ Key
- ❑ Locket
- ❑ Mouse
- ❑ Pen
- ❑ Pencil
- ❑ Skateboard
- ❑ Sock
- ❑ Tent
- ❑ Umbrella

In another room in the old house, the two kids found an ancient family album. Whose pictures do you think were inside? Before you can open it, you must find the following objects.

❑ Arrow
❑ Banana
❑ Bear
❑ Cactus
❑ Cane
☑ Cat
❑ Deer
❑ Fork
❑ Frog
❑ Giraffe
❑ Heart
❑ Ice-cream cone

❑ Monkey
❑ Mouse
❑ Owl
❑ Pencil
❑ Pig
❑ Rabbit
❑ Ring
❑ Rooster
❑ Saw
❑ Skull
❑ Snake
❑ Star

Wow! What a surprise! It is a photo album full of monsters!
On the first page, there is a picture of young Frankenstein on
his first date. Do you know which monster is on the next page?
Before you look, find the following hidden objects:

❑ Airplane   ❑ Hearts (4)   ❑ Snake
❑ Automobile   ❑ House   ❑ Surfboard
❑ Butterfly   ❑ Kite   ❑ Sword
❑ Camera   ❑ Light bulb   ❑ Tent
❑ Candle   ❑ Owl   ❑ Toothpaste
❑ Cup   ❑ Pencil   ❑ Tree
❑ Drum   ❑ Ring   ❑ Turtle
❑ Eyeglasses   ❑ Rocket   ❑ Umbrella
❑ Fish   ❑ Sailboat   ❑ Whistle

Wasn't Count Dracula a cuddly little critter? He loved to hide things. Can you find everything that he has hidden?

- Carrot
- Clown
- Coffeepot
- Comb
- Crown
- Elephant
- Fish
- Flashlight
- Flower
- Flying bats (10)
- Football
- Ghost
- Heart
- Hockey stick
- Hot dog
- Ice-cream cone
- Igloo
- Jack-o'-lantern
- Key
- Kite
- Mushroom
- Paintbrush
- Pencil
- Pizza
- Pyramid
- Sailor hat
- Top hat

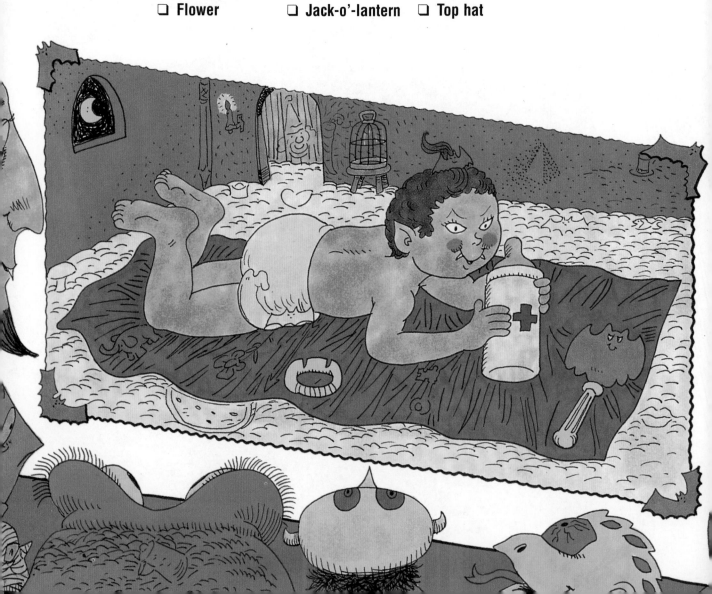

This is the largest picture in the monster family album. It is the abominable snow kid building snow monsters. He has also thrown in some hidden pictures. Look closely to find them all.

- ❏ Alligator
- ❏ Banana
- ❏ Bow tie
- ❏ Cactus
- ❏ Can
- ❏ Candle
- ❏ Cheese
- ❏ Chef's hat
- ❏ Cowboy hat
- ❏ Duck
- ❏ Fish
- ❏ Ghost
- ❏ Heart
- ❏ Hot dog
- ❏ Ice-cream cone
- ❏ Ice skate
- ❏ Ladder
- ❏ Lamp
- ❏ Lion
- ❏ Mouse
- ❏ Paintbrush
- ❏ Picture frame
- ❏ Pie
- ❏ Pig
- ❏ Pirate
- ❏ Shoe
- ❏ Shovel
- ❏ Top hat
- ❏ Umbrella
- ❏ Watering can

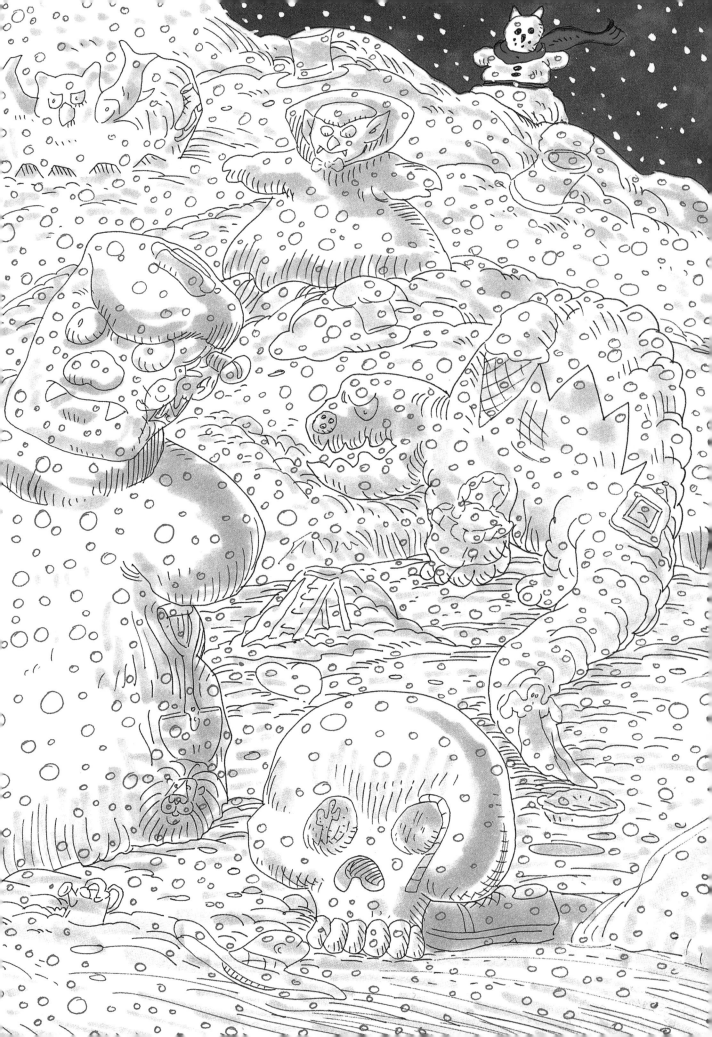

Here is the mummy, showing off his childhood pictures. You sure can get wrapped up in them! You also can get wrapped up in looking for the following hidden objects.

- ❑ Apple
- ❑ Arrow
- ❑ Artist
- ❑ Bird
- ❑ Blimp
- ❑ Bone
- ❑ Book
- ❑ Cupcake
- ❑ Drum
- ❑ Fish
- ❑ Football
- ❑ Ghost
- ❑ Golf club
- ❑ Hammer
- ❑ Kangaroo
- ❑ Kite
- ❑ Owl
- ❑ Pinocchio
- ❑ Sailor hat
- ❑ Saw
- ❑ Scarecrow
- ❑ Wagon

These are really terrific pictures—the best in the album! They are, of course, pictures of the invisible man throughout the years. Try to find the following objects:

- ❏ Banana
- ❏ Basket
- ❏ Bone
- ❏ Carrot
- ❏ Cheese
- ❏ Evergreen tree
- ❏ Fire hydrant
- ❏ Football
- ❏ Graduation cap
- ❏ Guitar
- ❏ Hamburger
- ❏ Heart
- ❏ Hot dog
- ❏ Ice-cream soda
- ❏ Light bulb
- ❏ Mouse
- ❏ Pear
- ❏ Pencil
- ❏ Rose
- ❏ Screwdriver
- ❏ Shovel
- ❏ Snail
- ❏ Star
- ❏ Television
- ❏ Tent
- ❏ Turtle
- ❏ Unicorn

FIRST BIRTHDAY ↴

KID LEAGUE STAR ↴

FIRST DAY OF SCHOOL ↴

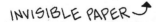

INVISIBLE PAPER ↴

SCHOOL FIELD TRIP ⤴

SOCCER CHAMP ⤵

TALKING TO SANTA ⤵

FIRST INVISIBLE MAN ON THE MOON ⤴

One picture is too big to fit into the album.
It's so big, it's hiding the following hidden pictures:

- Balloons (2)
- Birdhouse
- Birds (2)
- Boat
- Clock
- Coffeepot
- Covered wagon
- Crown
- Dog
- Elephant
- Fish (3)
- Hearts (2)
- Horseshoe
- Jack-o'-lantern
- Key
- Kite
- Mailbox
- Mermaid
- Old radio
- Old sock
- Old tire
- Pizza
- Tepee
- Worm

A MONSTER FAMILY PICNIC.

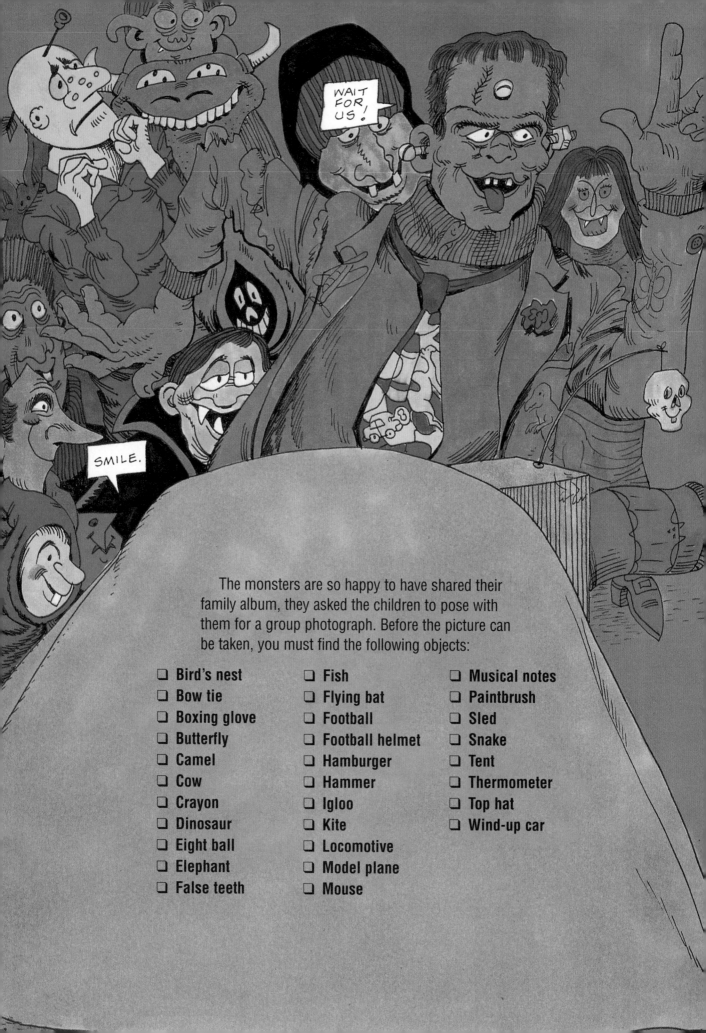

The monsters are so happy to have shared their family album, they asked the children to pose with them for a group photograph. Before the picture can be taken, you must find the following objects:

- ❑ Bird's nest
- ❑ Bow tie
- ❑ Boxing glove
- ❑ Butterfly
- ❑ Camel
- ❑ Cow
- ❑ Crayon
- ❑ Dinosaur
- ❑ Eight ball
- ❑ Elephant
- ❑ False teeth

- ❑ Fish
- ❑ Flying bat
- ❑ Football
- ❑ Football helmet
- ❑ Hamburger
- ❑ Hammer
- ❑ Igloo
- ❑ Kite
- ❑ Locomotive
- ❑ Model plane
- ❑ Mouse

- ❑ Musical notes
- ❑ Paintbrush
- ❑ Sled
- ❑ Snake
- ❑ Tent
- ❑ Thermometer
- ❑ Top hat
- ❑ Wind-up car

Early one morning, Frankie has a brilliant idea. He decides to visit some friends he hasn't seen in a long time.

FIND FRANKIE IN HIS NUTTY NEIGHBORHOOD, AND THESE FUN ITEMS:

- ❑ Book
- ❑ Bowling ball
- ❑ Bucket
- ❑ Candle
- ❑ Dog
- ❑ Duck
- ❑ Fish (3)
- ❑ Flying bats (3)
- ❑ Football helmet
- ❑ Hammer
- ❑ Heart
- ❑ Jack-o'-lantern
- ❑ Moose head
- ❑ Periscope
- ❑ Pinocchio
- ❑ Raincoat
- ❑ Roller skates
- ❑ Sailor hat
- ❑ Scarecrow
- ❑ Skier
- ❑ Skull
- ❑ Star
- ❑ Tepee
- ❑ Thermometer
- ❑ Tulip
- ❑ Turtle
- ❑ Watering can
- ❑ Wreath

Frankie first looks for his old, old friend Manny Mummy in a place with lots of sand.

FIND MANNY MUMMY IN THE DRY DESERT, AND THESE FUN ITEMS:

- ❏ Balloons (3)
- ❏ Banana peel
- ❏ Bathtub
- ❏ Birdhouse
- ❏ Brooms (2)
- ❏ Earring
- ❏ Fire hydrant
- ❏ Fish (2)
- ❏ Flower
- ❏ Gas pump
- ❏ Ring
- ❏ Sailor hat
- ❏ Sand castle
- ❏ Sand pail
- ❏ Sled
- ❏ Slingshot
- ❏ Snake
- ❏ Snowman
- ❏ Soccer ball
- ❏ Star
- ❏ Straw
- ❏ Suitcase
- ❏ Surfboard
- ❏ Turtle
- ❏ TV antenna
- ❏ Umbrella
- ❏ Watering can
- ❏ Watermelon slice

Frankie and Manny Mummy set off to find their friend Batty Bat. He lives in a strange place.

FIND BATTY BAT IN TERRIFYING TRANSYLVANIA, AND THESE FUN ITEMS:

- ❑ Alligator
- ❑ Arrows (2)
- ❑ Baker
- ❑ Bones (6)
- ❑ Book
- ❑ Bride and groom
- ❑ Broken heart
- ❑ Broken mirror
- ❑ Candle
- ❑ Dog
- ❑ Fish
- ❑ Flower
- ❑ Football
- ❑ Fortune teller
- ❑ Hair dryer
- ❑ Kite
- ❑ Lion
- ❑ Mouse
- ❑ Nail
- ❑ Octopus
- ❑ Rabbit
- ❑ Scissors
- ❑ Skulls (4)
- ❑ Top hat
- ❑ Training wheels
- ❑ Umbrella
- ❑ Vulture
- ❑ Worm

Now they are off to find another pal. This one lives in a swamp!

FIND SWAMPY SAM IN THIS MUSHY MARSH, AND THESE FUN ITEMS:

- ❑ Apple
- ❑ Cupcake
- ❑ Drum
- ❑ Football helmet
- ❑ Fork
- ❑ Frog
- ❑ Grand piano
- ❑ Hammer
- ❑ Key
- ❑ Lost boot
- ❑ Lost mitten
- ❑ Medal
- ❑ Necktie
- ❑ Palm tree
- ❑ Pencil
- ❑ Pizza slice
- ❑ Quarter moon
- ❑ Ring
- ❑ Snake
- ❑ Soccer ball
- ❑ Sock
- ❑ Speaker
- ❑ Spoon
- ❑ Toothbrush
- ❑ Trumpet
- ❑ Umbrellas (2)

Warren Werewolf is Frankie's next friend to find. He plays baseball with the Dead End Dodgers.

FIND WARREN WEREWOLF AT THE BALLPARK, AND THESE FUN ITEMS:

- ❑ Bicycle horn
- ❑ Bone
- ❑ Cactus
- ❑ Candy cane
- ❑ Carrot
- ❑ Cookie
- ❑ Crown
- ❑ Empty can
- ❑ Eyeglasses (2)
- ❑ Feather
- ❑ Fir tree
- ❑ Flamingo
- ❑ Footprint
- ❑ Frog
- ❑ Heart
- ❑ Horseshoe
- ❑ Humpty Dumpty
- ❑ Kite
- ❑ Lamp
- ❑ Pliers
- ❑ Six-fingered glove
- ❑ Skull
- ❑ Squirrel
- ❑ Tic-tac-toe
- ❑ Witch
- ❑ Worm

Frankie and his pals go to an old school-house, where their friend Lena Lightning is a student.

FIND LENA LIGHTNING AMONG HER CREEPY CLASSMATES, AND THESE FUN ITEMS:

- ❑ Apple core
- ❑ Bell
- ❑ Bone tree
- ❑ Broken mirror
- ❑ Cactus
- ❑ Candles (3)
- ❑ Crystal ball
- ❑ Egg
- ❑ Firecracker
- ❑ Flashlight
- ❑ Flying bats (3)
- ❑ Fortune teller
- ❑ Hot dog
- ❑ Ice skate
- ❑ Mask
- ❑ Mouse
- ❑ Necktie
- ❑ Owl
- ❑ Pencil
- ❑ Saw
- ❑ Shark fin
- ❑ Skateboard
- ❑ Skunk
- ❑ Snakes (2)
- ❑ Star
- ❑ Vulture
- ❑ Worm

Next, Frankie and his friends set out to visit Greta Ghost, but none of her neighbors has seen her in a while.

FIND FRANKIE AND HIS OTHER FRIENDS AT GRETA'S HAUNTED HOUSE, AND THESE FUN ITEMS:

- ❑ Alligator
- ❑ Arrows (2)
- ❑ Axe
- ❑ Balloons (5)
- ❑ Banana peel
- ❑ Bowling ball
- ❑ Broom
- ❑ Cup
- ❑ Dart
- ❑ Drum
- ❑ Fork
- ❑ Hammer
- ❑ Hatched egg
- ❑ Heart
- ❑ Keys (2)
- ❑ Ring
- ❑ Screwdriver
- ❑ Ski
- ❑ Stool
- ❑ Sword
- ❑ Teapot
- ❑ Tepee
- ❑ Torn sock
- ❑ Turtle
- ❑ Umbrella
- ❑ Wreath

Frankie can't find Greta Ghost at the haunted house, so he and his friends check the new condos.

FIND GRETA GHOST IN MODERN MONSTERVILLE, AND THESE FUN ITEMS:

- ❑ Arrow
- ❑ Balloons (4)
- ❑ Bones (2)
- ❑ Camel
- ❑ Candles (3)
- ❑ Fire hydrant
- ❑ Fish (3)
- ❑ Flowers (3)
- ❑ Football helmet
- ❑ Frog
- ❑ Hoe
- ❑ Horseshoe
- ❑ Ice-cream cone
- ❑ Igloo
- ❑ Kites (2)
- ❑ Lollipop
- ❑ Lost bathing trunks
- ❑ Lost boot
- ❑ Mice (3)
- ❑ Painted egg
- ❑ Periscope
- ❑ Pyramid
- ❑ Quarter moon
- ❑ Rabbit
- ❑ Roller skates
- ❑ Sea horse
- ❑ Seal
- ❑ Sunglasses (2)

Together at last, the friends go on a picnic—where else but in a cemetery?

FIND FRANKIE AND HIS FRIENDS IN THIS GHOULISH GRAVEYARD, AND THESE FUN ITEMS:

- ❑ Apron
- ❑ Baseball cap
- ❑ Broom
- ❑ Bucket
- ❑ Burned-out candle
- ❑ Chef's hat
- ❑ Clothespin
- ❑ Crown
- ❑ Fish (2)
- ❑ Flower
- ❑ Guitar
- ❑ Heart
- ❑ House
- ❑ Light bulb
- ❑ Mice (2)
- ❑ Paintbrush
- ❑ Picture frame
- ❑ Pig
- ❑ Ring
- ❑ Shovel
- ❑ Spoon
- ❑ Straw
- ❑ Tire
- ❑ Truck
- ❑ TV antenna
- ❑ Worm
- ❑ Wristwatch

After the picnic, Frankie and his friends go to see—you guessed it!—a monster movie.

FIND FRANKIE AND HIS FRIENDS AT THIS FRIGHTENING FLICK, AND THESE FUN ITEMS:

- ❑ Apple core
- ❑ Arrow
- ❑ Crown
- ❑ Dog
- ❑ Drum
- ❑ Eight ball
- ❑ Eyeglasses
- ❑ Faucet
- ❑ Fish skeleton
- ❑ Flashlight
- ❑ Fortune teller
- ❑ Heart
- ❑ Ice-cream pop
- ❑ Necktie
- ❑ Oilcan
- ❑ Paper airplane
- ❑ Periscope
- ❑ Piggy bank
- ❑ Rabbit
- ❑ Roller skates
- ❑ Sailboat
- ❑ Skunk
- ❑ Star
- ❑ Superhero
- ❑ Toast
- ❑ Top hat
- ❑ Trash can
- ❑ Trumpet
- ❑ Worm

While walking back from the movie, Frankie and his friends see a frightening sight!

FIND FRANKIE AND HIS FRIENDS WITH THESE TERRIFIC TRICK-OR-TREATERS, AND THESE FUN ITEMS:

- ❑ Balloon
- ❑ Broom
- ❑ Butterfly
- ❑ Candy cane
- ❑ Carrot
- ❑ Chef's hat
- ❑ Crown
- ❑ Earmuffs
- ❑ Fork
- ❑ Key
- ❑ Mustache
- ❑ Paintbrush
- ❑ Paper bag
- ❑ Pencil
- ❑ Pizza
- ❑ Roller skates
- ❑ Sailor hat
- ❑ Sock
- ❑ Star
- ❑ Top hat
- ❑ Tree ornament
- ❑ Umbrella
- ❑ Watering can
- ❑ Worm

It is time for Frankie and friends to say good-bye—for now, that is. They have planned to get together soon, and you are invited to join them!

FIND FRANKIE, MANNY MUMMY, BATTY BAT, SWAMPY SAM, WARREN WEREWOLF, LENA LIGHTNING, GRETA GHOST, AND THESE FUN ITEMS:

- ❑ Apple core
- ❑ Arrow
- ❑ Baseball
- ❑ Bone
- ❑ Crayon
- ❑ Flowerpot
- ❑ Frog
- ❑ Heart
- ❑ Kite
- ❑ Owl
- ❑ Turtle
- ❑ Worm

WELCOME!

So you have decided to enter! Join our fearless friends, who have come to explore Creepy Castle, too. Waiting for them at the bottom of a long staircase is a fire-breathing dragon! Can you see these hidden objects?

- ❑ Apple
- ❑ Arrow
- ❑ Balloon
- ❑ Bone
- ❑ Book
- ❑ Cat
- ❑ Comb
- ❑ Donkey's head
- ❑ Envelope
- ❑ Fire hydrant
- ❑ Fish
- ❑ Fork
- ❑ Guitar
- ❑ Heart
- ❑ Jack-o'-lantern
- ❑ Magnifying glass
- ❑ Medal
- ❑ Paintbrush
- ❑ Spear
- ❑ Sword
- ❑ Tricycle
- ❑ Turtle

Racing through a partly open curtain, our friends enter the room of a famous monster star, who has hidden all kinds of things. Can you find them?

- ❑ Automobile
- ❑ Axe
- ❑ Basket
- ❑ Bird
- ❑ Bone
- ❑ Candle
- ❑ Cups (2)
- ❑ Elephant
- ❑ Fish
- ❑ Flower
- ❑ Flying bat
- ❑ Guitar
- ❑ Hammer
- ❑ Hearts (2)
- ❑ Igloo
- ❑ Kangaroo
- ❑ Mermaid
- ❑ Mitten
- ❑ Mouse
- ❑ Party hat
- ❑ Pencil
- ❑ Quarter moon
- ❑ Rabbit
- ❑ Star
- ❑ Toothbrush
- ❑ Tugboat
- ❑ Whale

Now here is a weird sight—a headless knight! Could he be related to the Headless Horseman of Sleepy Hollow? Before going on, find these hidden pictures.

- ❏ Baseball bat
- ❏ Book
- ❏ Bottle
- ❏ Cow's head
- ❏ Cupcake
- ❏ Duck
- ❏ Eagle's head
- ❏ Ear of corn
- ❏ Envelope
- ❏ Feather
- ❏ Frog
- ❏ Ghost
- ❏ Hot dog
- ❏ Key
- ❏ Paper clip
- ❏ Pea pod
- ❏ Saw
- ❏ Shoe
- ❏ Toothbrush
- ❏ Turtle
- ❏ Umbrella
- ❏ Wheelbarrow

What lurks beneath this new knight's hood? Is he a handsome hero or another creepy creature? Before you turn the page to find out, look for the following hidden pictures.

- Arrow
- Astronaut
- Banana
- Cactus
- Carrot
- Crab
- Electric guitar
- Fish

- Heart
- Helicopter
- Hot dog
- Ice-cream cone
- Invisible knight
- Key
- Kite
- Parachute

- Pelican
- Rocket
- Sailboat
- Skis
- Teapot
- Toothbrush
- Truck
- Turtle

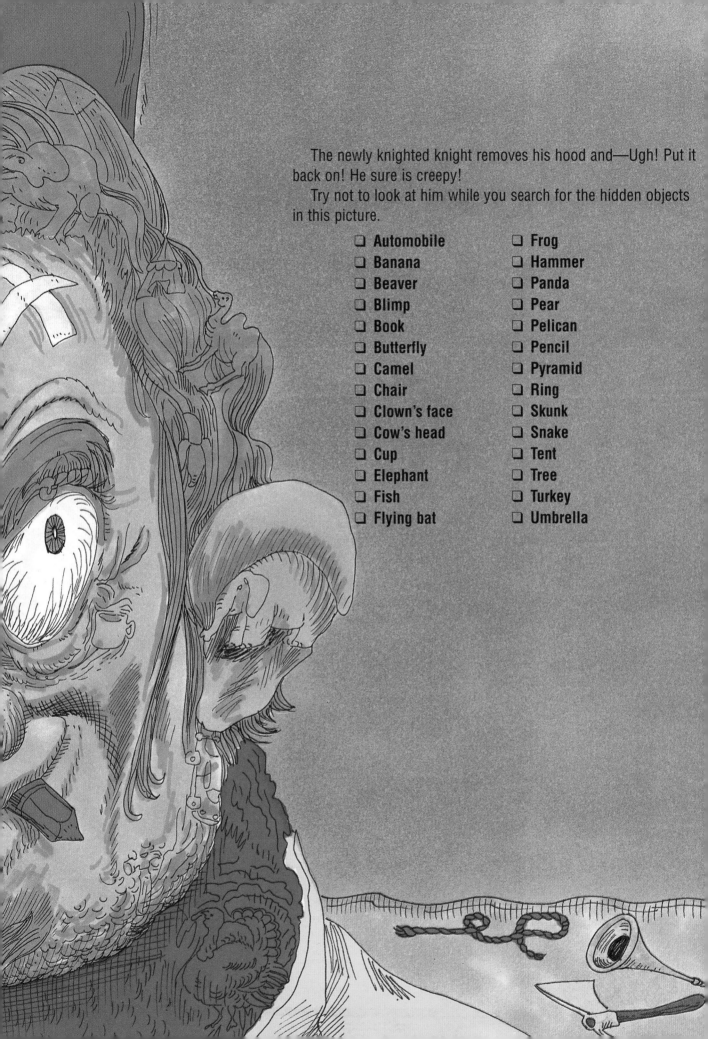

The newly knighted knight removes his hood and—Ugh! Put it back on! He sure is creepy!

Try not to look at him while you search for the hidden objects in this picture.

- ❑ Automobile
- ❑ Banana
- ❑ Beaver
- ❑ Blimp
- ❑ Book
- ❑ Butterfly
- ❑ Camel
- ❑ Chair
- ❑ Clown's face
- ❑ Cow's head
- ❑ Cup
- ❑ Elephant
- ❑ Fish
- ❑ Flying bat
- ❑ Frog
- ❑ Hammer
- ❑ Panda
- ❑ Pear
- ❑ Pelican
- ❑ Pencil
- ❑ Pyramid
- ❑ Ring
- ❑ Skunk
- ❑ Snake
- ❑ Tent
- ❑ Tree
- ❑ Turkey
- ❑ Umbrella

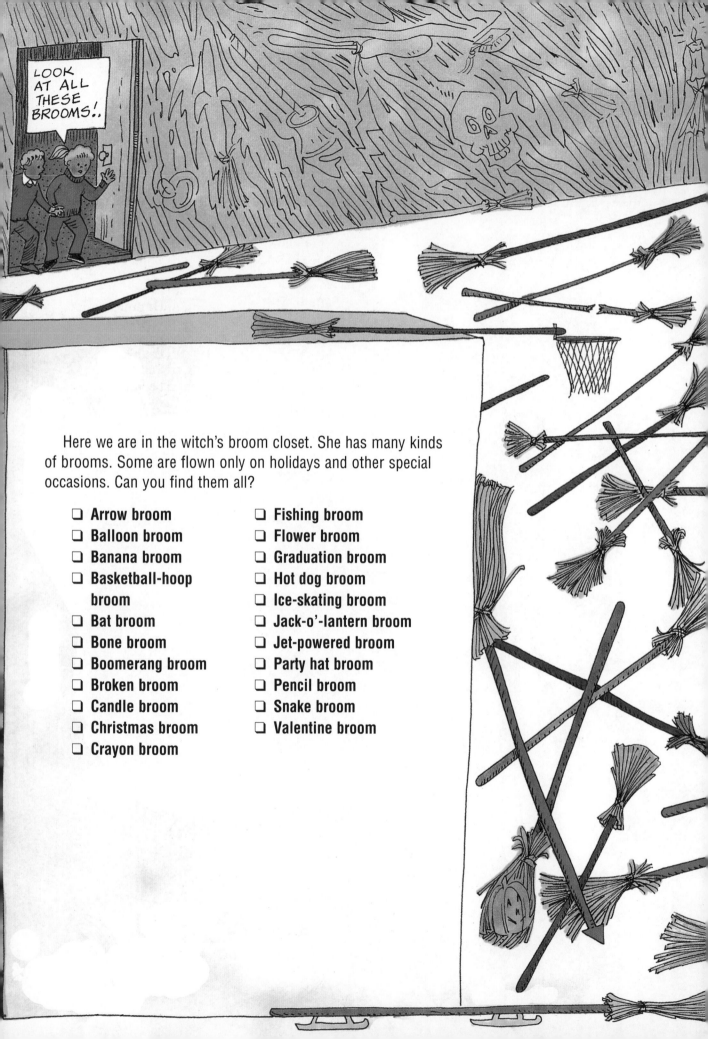

LOOK AT ALL THESE BROOMS!.

Here we are in the witch's broom closet. She has many kinds of brooms. Some are flown only on holidays and other special occasions. Can you find them all?

- ❑ Arrow broom
- ❑ Balloon broom
- ❑ Banana broom
- ❑ Basketball-hoop broom
- ❑ Bat broom
- ❑ Bone broom
- ❑ Boomerang broom
- ❑ Broken broom
- ❑ Candle broom
- ❑ Christmas broom
- ❑ Crayon broom
- ❑ Fishing broom
- ❑ Flower broom
- ❑ Graduation broom
- ❑ Hot dog broom
- ❑ Ice-skating broom
- ❑ Jack-o'-lantern broom
- ❑ Jet-powered broom
- ❑ Party hat broom
- ❑ Pencil broom
- ❑ Snake broom
- ❑ Valentine broom

Through a hole in the wall, our friends take a peek at Wizard Merlin as he creates nasty nightmares.

Peek carefully at this picture and find the following hidden objects.

- ❑ Airplane
- ❑ Apple
- ❑ Arrow
- ❑ Axe
- ❑ Bat
- ❑ Drum
- ❑ Elephant's head
- ❑ Football
- ❑ Ghost
- ❑ Gorilla
- ❑ Hearts (3)
- ❑ Helicopter
- ❑ Horse's head
- ❑ Ice-cream cone
- ❑ Kite
- ❑ Lion's face
- ❑ Lizard
- ❑ Magnet
- ❑ Mask
- ❑ Mouse
- ❑ Mushroom
- ❑ Octopus
- ❑ Owl
- ❑ Paintbrush
- ❑ Shark
- ❑ Skull
- ❑ Snake
- ❑ Top hat
- ❑ Toucan
- ❑ Windmill

Surprise! Our fearless friends have been invited to a party in their honor. Looks like they are having a creepy, crazy good time!

You can join in the fun by finding the following hidden pictures.

- ❑ Arrows (2)
- ❑ Bottle
- ❑ Cup
- ❑ Fish
- ❑ Flower
- ❑ Flying bat
- ❑ Fork
- ❑ Ghosts (2)
- ❑ Hot dog
- ❑ Ice skate
- ❑ Key
- ❑ Kite
- ❑ Light bulb
- ❑ Mitten
- ❑ Musical notes
- ❑ Pencil
- ❑ Penguin
- ❑ Piggy bank
- ❑ Pinwheel
- ❑ Rocket
- ❑ Rocking chair
- ❑ Roller skate
- ❑ Seal
- ❑ Sock
- ❑ Spoon
- ❑ Toothbrush

I WAS CROWNED PRINCE!

Congratulations! You have survived Creepy Castle! But what crazy gifts have our friends brought home?

See if you can find these peculiar presents hidden in the picture below.

- ❑ Barbell
- ❑ Broken clock
- ❑ Cactus
- ❑ Dog
- ❑ Fire hydrant
- ❑ Fountain
- ❑ Heart
- ❑ Ice-cream cone
- ❑ Key
- ❑ Kite
- ❑ Pirate
- ❑ Sailboat
- ❑ Television
- ❑ Tennis racket
- ❑ Tire
- ❑ Yo-yo

THEY'VE RETURNED FROM CREEPY CASTLE!

WHAT DO THEY HAVE?